What's Missing?

by Niki Yektai

illustrated by Susannah Ryan

Clarion Books
TICKNOR & FIELDS: A HOUGHTON MIFFLIN COMPANY
New York

Clarion Books
Ticknor & Fields, a Houghton Mifflin Company
Text copyright © 1987 by Niki Yektai
Illustrations copyright © 1987 by Susannah Ryan

Library of Congress Cataloging-in-Publication Data

Yektai, Niki.
What's missing?
Summary: Readers find what's missing in a picture
when the page is turned. Example: a girl depicted
pedaling in mid-air is missing a bicycle.
1. Children's questions and answers.
[1. Questions and answers]   I. Ryan, Susannah, ill.
II. Title.
AG195.Y45   1987   031'.02   87-784
ISBN 0-89919-510-5

NI   10   9   8   7   6   5   4   3   2   1

For Helen McCabe, the best baby nurse in the world.
—N.Y.
_____
To M., D., and J. L.C.
—S.R.

What's missing?

The bicycle!

What else is missing?

The dog!

Now what's missing?

The slide!

What else is missing?

The seesaw!

What's missing?

The clothes!

What else is missing?

The ice cream!

Now what's missing?

The house!

What else is missing?

The T.V.!

What's missing?

The silverware!

What else is missing?

The water!

Now what's missing?

The book!

What else is missing?

The bear!

What's missing?

The bed!

Is everything all right?

Good-night.